Planet Food

by Kathryn L. O'Dell
illustrated by Jack Snider

Farid and Farah were brother and sister. They were a lot alike. They loved to play, they liked school, and they liked to eat. There was one problem. They didn't like to eat healthy food, and they loved junk food.

Their parents would always say, "You have to eat your vegetables. Please eat some fruit!"

But Farid and Farah would always say, "We want candy bars! We want cookies!"

One day, Farid and Farah went to a carnival. They had a lot of fun. They rode on rides, and they ate a lot of junk food. It was starting to get late.

"Well, it's time to go home," their dad said. "You've had enough junk food today. We're going to go to the grocery store. We're going to get food for a healthy dinner!"

This upset Farid and Farah. They wanted more junk food.

Then Farah saw the sign for a ride.
She said, "Look! A spaceship ride!"

"Can we go on the spaceship?" asked Farid.

Their mom said, "Okay. One more ride,
and then we're leaving."

Farid and Farah boarded the spaceship.
It went very high. When they were at the top,
they thought they'd come back down. But the
spaceship went higher, and higher, and higher.
Soon the kids were floating in outer space!

Finally, the spaceship landed with a crash. It landed on a planet far, far away. The kids got out of the spaceship. They were standing in Raspberry River.

"Where are we?" asked Farid.

"I don't know," said Farah, "but it looks like a planet that's all food!"

They got out of the river. They licked their hands. "Hmm," said Farah, "this tastes pretty good."

"You're right," said Farid. "But let's go look for some candy! This food planet must be full of candy!"

"Okay," said Farah. "Look over there! Bikes."

The bikes were made of broccoli! Farid and Farah rode them down Apple Avenue and Strawberry Street. Then they rode up a mountain. "Maybe there's some candy at the top!" said Farah.

They got to the top of the mountain, and they didn't see any candy. They were very hungry and very tired. They ate some broccoli from the bikes. "Hmm," said Farid, "this is really good."

9

"Look!" Farah said, pointing down. "This mountain is made of avocados!"

"I really want some candy," said Farid.

Suddenly, they started to slide down the mountain. They were in an avocado avalanche!

They landed in Scrambled Eggs Swamp. "Now what are we going to do?" asked Farah.

"Look!" said Farid. "There's a castle! There has to be candy in there!" They pulled themselves out of the swamp and walked to the castle.

When they got close to the castle, they could see that it was made of carrots. "Carrots! Yuck!" said Farid. But they ate some anyway because they were very, very hungry.

"Hmm," said Farah, "these are tasty."

They went into the castle. They were
exhausted and wanted to sit down. Farah
sat on a cantaloupe couch, and Farid sat
in a cheese chair. They started eating
the furniture. "Hmm," said Farid, "this
cheese is delicious."

They looked all over the castle, but they couldn't find any candy. "I really want a cookie!" said Farah. "Let's go outside. Maybe there is a cookie tree by the castle."

They went outside, but they didn't see a cookie tree. "I'm thirsty," said Farid. "Let's look for some soda to drink."

Farid and Farah didn't find any soda. But they found Lemon Lake. The lake was made of lemonade. "Let's try this," said Farid.

"Hmm," said Farah, "this is fantastic!" Then they swam in Lemon Lake.

After they swam, they sat on Blueberry Beach and ate some blueberries. "Wow!" said Farid. "These are yummy! You know, I have a lot of energy from all of this good food."

"Me too," said Farah. "Let's play!"

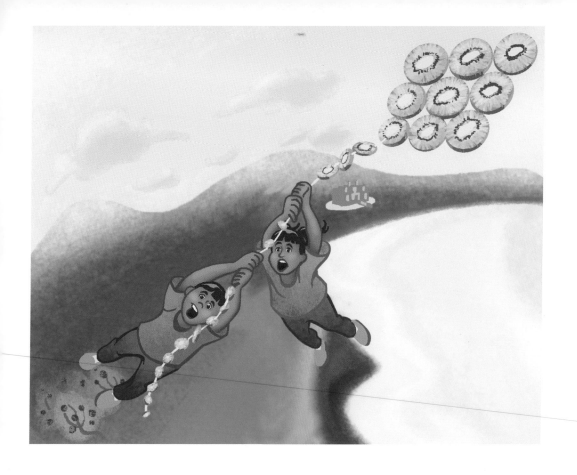

Farah saw a kiwi kite. "Let's fly that kite," she said. She grabbed the kite, and it started to go up in the sky. "Help! Help me!"

Farid grabbed on to the kite. They couldn't stop it. It went higher, and higher, and higher. It pulled them up into outer space.

The kite went faster and faster.
"Look!" said Farah. "We're going home!"
They landed in another spaceship at
the carnival. They climbed out and found
their parents.

"How was the ride?" their mom asked.

"It was unbelievable!" said Farah.

"Yes," said Farid, "it was out of this world!"

"Great!" said their dad. "Now let's go to the grocery store. I'm hungry."

At the grocery store, Farid and Farah didn't even look at junk food. The fruits and vegetables looked delicious.

"Let's get some blueberries, and raspberries, and broccoli!" said Farid.

"Look!" said Farah. "Avocados! I love those!"

"What's going on?" their parents asked. But the kids just laughed and loaded the cart with their new favorite foods.